HOW TO
TREAT
YOUR
PREGNANT
WIFE

A COMMON-SENSE GUIDE

HOW TO TREAT YOUR PREGNANT WIFE

MICHAEL J. SNAPP

WALNUT SPRINGS PRESS

To all the selfless moms, but especially to my mom,
my wife's mom, and ultimately to my wife. The coolest,
greatest, most important thing I've ever done or will ever do is
to be a dad and husband. Thank you, Kimie.

Walnut Springs Press, LLC
110 South 800 West
Brigham City, Utah 84302
walnutspringspress.blogspot.com

Text copyright © 2012 by Michael J. Snapp
Illustrations copyright © 2012 by Bo Kihye Park
Cover design copyright © 2012 by Walnut Springs Press
Interior design copyright © 2012 by Walnut Springs Press

ISBN: 978-1-59992-808-1

Acknowledgements

Thank you to Jeni and Brad Neel, Amber and Russell Collins, Laura and Kyle Dugovic, Cristian and Jeff Erickson, Sharon Bluth, and Andrea and Douglas Gardner for reviewing my rough drafts, offering feedback, and regularly asking me how the book was coming along. Thank you, Cary Boone Jones, for helping me realize this book could help more people than I thought. Michelle Taylor, thank you for unknowingly always saying the right thing at the right time ("You should write a book, Michael"). Thank you, Patrick Combs, for inspiring me to follow my passion, and for showing genuine interest in me and my hopes even though you didn't know me. Finally, thanks to Melanie and Jack R. Christianson for your review, assistance, friendship, and encouragement. Thank you, Linda Prince, for your amazing editing, care, and professionalism; Amy Orton for your design and vision; and Walnut Springs Press for giving me this opportunity.

Introduction

I got the idea for this book seven years ago when my wife, Kimie, was pregnant with our fifth child. In a ten-minute period, there were three signs she needed extra help with things. First, she was changing her clothes in our bedroom before going to a meeting. As she finished, we heard our four-year-old yelling for her. Kimie gave me an exhausted look and then hid in our closet. Thinking I was funny, I showed our son where she was hiding, and he dragged her out. The second sign was when our twenty-month-old son walked in yelling, "Mama," and Kimie whispered, "Go away." She didn't mean it, but me being as quick as I am, I realized she was at the end of her rope. Ten minutes later, I saw the third sign. We were saying family prayers, and our eight-year-old daughter informed Kimie that the twenty-month-old was "poopy." To be sure, Kimie bent down, pulled his pants away from his back, and sniffed. When she stood up, I said, "You're about to lose it, aren't you?" The look my wife gave me suggested I had been clueless for a long time. It welcomed me to her reality. Did I mention she was also a full-time college student?

Kimie was not the only mother who was at the end of her rope. Earlier that day, she told me she was visiting a friend who was also buried with children, a myriad of other responsibilities, and life in general. Kimie told her it would be nice if she could just hide for a while. I decided to try to make life easier for my pregnant wife. (Not bad, right? It only took the fifth pregnancy for me to realize this.) I started jotting down simple notes to remind myself of things I needed to do for her. Soon, I realized there were countless things I could do to make her life easier. And while I didn't originally intend to put them in a book, I knew I couldn't be the only man who needed these reminders.

Understand, we shouldn't do these things because we feel our wives can't, but because they deserve to have us do them in their place, or in our own place sometimes. Seriously, who said it is the wife's job to do all the tedious household chores? I know that attitude exists. Some men even preach it. I hope this book will help bring about a paradigm shift.

If after reading these ideas you say, "Are you kidding me? I can't do all that," stop and ask yourself how your wife has been able to do it all—while pregnant! If you can't do everything mentioned, or if some things aren't applicable, do as much as you can, as often as you can. Your wife will like it.

Some of the ideas in this book include detailed explanations or real-life examples, while others don't, because they are self-explanatory. After all, this is common sense. What is common sense? *Webster's Universal Dictionary and Thesaurus* defines common sense as "ordinary, practical good sense; good judgment." According to Merriam-Webster's online dictionary, common sense is "sound and prudent judgment based on a simple perception of the situation or facts." I like to focus on the "simple perception" part. It's embarrassingly simple. As to the ideas in this book, it's not that your wife can't do these things, or won't do them. But think about it—we all enjoy having things done for us. We could make dinner for ourselves every night, but when our wife makes dinner, it tastes better simply because she did it for us. Dinner is always better if you're not the one who had to stand over that oven and then clean up the kitchen.

Lastly, before you continue reading this book, please consider the following scripture: "When I was a child, I spake as a child, I understood as a child, I thought as a child: but when I became a man, I put away childish things" (1 Corinthians 13:11). Step up and be a man, and put away the childish things—thoughts, attitudes, habits, etc.—that stand in the way of you truly respecting your wife, especially now that she is pregnant. And ladies, please appreciate your husbands' attempts and don't take them for granted. Men, I promise they will appreciate you, and you will grow closer.

MONTH 1

Don't come home from work and ask, "What's for dinner?"

You know, I started to type an explanation for this one, but then decided not to. However, I do think that this question, asked by a man on a daily basis, would be equivalent to your wife asking you, every weekday at 5:00 AM, "So, will you be going to work again today?"

A friend of mine has something she appreciates of her husband. On days when he realizes she is feeling ill or extra tired, he simply steps in and makes PB&J sandwiches for himself and their son. He makes no issues of it, asks for nothing, and points nothing out. It's VERY simple and understated, but it speaks volumes to his wife.

Take the garbage out (this includes bedrooms, home office, bathrooms, etc.).

Yep, some women are expected to take the trash out. Some women are expected to take the trash out while they are pregnant. Truthfully, I don't think they are expected to; rather, I think we men overlook this, and women get tired of waiting for us to do it. Well, not anymore!

Don't say, "Do you really think you should be eating that?"

First off, she probably knows what she can and can't eat, and secondly, you're not her boss. Thirdly, she deserves some kind of comfort, and that may include comfort food (as she defines comfort food). Hey, why don't you offer her some of your Ding Dongs and the protein shake you recently picked up? Yep, you picked them up because YOU went to the store. We'll talk more about that later.

Don't, especially if this is your first baby, allow your wife to watch channels on cable that show risky childbirths.

My wife and I watched these shows, probably during every pregnancy. It's worse than watching a cooking show while experiencing the most wretched bout of food-poisoning ever. In other words, it doesn't help to watch this type of programming. Watching footage of risky (though modestly filmed) childbirths is much more than just a Maalox moment—it absolutely freaks your wife out, and you too. Don't do it. I guess to fully understand why, you will actually have to do it once. But please take my word for it—don't do it. If you do, it will make for an awfully long and dreadful nine months.

Don't speak in terms of "We need to …"

For example, don't say, "We need to get this house cleaner." This is condescending. Your wife knows what needs to be done, and when you use the pronoun "we," she will know you are pointing the finger directly at *her*. I put this in the first month so you can get in the habit of doing it right, if you haven't already. You really need to get on this one!

Admit it. When you say something like, "We really need to clean this house," what you honestly hope happens is that she will get up off her fanny and get that house cleaned before you get home from work. News flash—she feels like that's what you're saying!

Anytime Tips

❀ Take a minute and consider how you
   speak to your wife.

Remember that your wife is extra-emotional and touchy
while she is pregnant, so some things that normally
wouldn't be rude are very rude in this situation. But hold
on, that's not the point. Why do we men ever speak rudely,
condescendingly, sarcastically, or in any other unloving way
to our wives? Break this habit before you break her heart,
and before you have children who will hear you do it.

❀ Gas up the car for her.

Don't tell her you did. You don't need a pat on the back.
See, this is an easy one.

🐾 Get out of "your" recliner and let her
  sit in it.

Hey, Your Majesty, have you ever considered "letting" your wife sit in "your" recliner? Make sure she has the most comfortable place to sit, lie down, or whatever—every time, everywhere. You should only sit down after she does anyway. She should choose first, period.

🐾 If you had a hamburger for lunch and
  she makes hamburgers for dinner,
  don't say, "Oh, shoot, I had a
  hamburger for lunch."

Wives don't like that. Honestly, this is far worse than telling a joke you're pretty sure nobody has heard before, just to have someone say, "Dude, that's been around awhile." I know, it has nothing to do with this common-sense item, but it is another example of "What were you thinking?" Still don't get it? Never mind—just don't make this mistake!

Consider the example you set in front of your kids.

Kind of like the last one. How will your children remember you treating their mother? Don't have other kids yet? So what. One's on the way—start acting appropriately now.

Keep a photo or video history of the pregnancy.

Take photos of your wife and baby growing. It's just another way to be involved with the whole process. It's fun to look back and see how your wife's tummy (women like "tummy," not "belly") has grown. Videotape the ultrasound (where allowed), etc. Our oldest child is seventeen years old, and we really enjoy looking back on those videos, as much for seeing our hair and clothes in the "old days" as anything else.

MONTH 2

If she forgot to do something she told you she was going to do (this can happen during pregnancy), don't call her on it.

Don't say, "I thought you said you were going to take care of . . ." First of all, that's condescending, and secondly she's pregnant, so give her a break. Your wife's hormones are doing strange and annoying things to her—they may even affect her memory.

The point here is to understand that she may be forgetful right now, and then calmly roll with it. Don't feel you need to correct her by bluntly reminding her of something she said she'd do. Instead, ask her, "Did you, by chance, but it is absolutely okay if you didn't get around to it, _____?" Then add, "If not, oh sweetest person on earth, I will do it." Use your own words and don't sound goofy or insincere.

Arrange a ladies night out for your wife.

As important as it is for you and your wife to spend time together, don't forget that she needs some time to hang out with friends. This should be happening regardless of pregnancy status, but it is quite important during the pregnancy. Why? Because after the baby is born, it will be a lot harder for her to spend time with friends, since she will need to heal from the delivery, nurse the baby, etc. Make ladies night happen for your wife. Get in the habit now and it just might get easier after the baby arrives.

Don't ask her how long it will take her to get back to her pre-pregnancy weight.

She may be concerned about this, but you certainly don't have to worry about it—or even worse, make her worry about it. If you ask her about this, you will give her the impression that you will be less attracted to her until she weighs what she did before she got pregnant.

Here's a little secret: Sometimes a woman never gets back to her pre-pregnancy weight. She gives up a lot bringing a baby into the world, including her body. Don't give her any grief about this—just promise her you will love her regardless. Hopefully, your marriage is based on many things above and beyond physical attraction. If not, you have some work to do. You need to get to know your wife, not just what she looks like. By way of reminder, she is beautiful! This weight thing is important, so it will show up throughout the book.

Don't say, "Eat up—you're eating for two now."

Pregnant ladies don't find this as humorous as nonpregnant gentlemen. Not to mention it's not even remotely close to being original. It's one of those dumb jokes you hear at a family reunion from someone who hasn't seen you since the last one, and he's trying to make small talk. If you must be funny, come up with something new, something that is your own. If you can't, just move on.

On a regular basis, play soft music in the house.

Put some soft, relaxing music on the stereo. It's soothing to your pregnant wife, and studies show it can actually bring about a calmer baby. Believe me, you want a calmer baby. But this is really about making a more relaxing atmosphere for your wife.

Anytime Tips

🪶 Ask your wife what she wants you to
make for dinner.

Yep, make dinner. Yep, for her, and you, and the kids. Yep, ask
what she wants you to make. Yep, it's going to be inconvenient.
Yep, you may get tired of doing it. Yep, I've done this. Nope,
I didn't enjoy doing it. Yep, my wife appreciated it, so it was
worth it. The dinner can be simple—the point is you have
taken away one more task from your wife.

🪶 This is tied to the last one—really
actually make the dinner.

Yes, I'm harping on this one quite a bit. This is a very tedious
chore. My wife likes to cook; she truly enjoys it. However,

trying to be creative and come up with three meals a day, seven days a week, gets old. I've tried this before and I'm frustrated two days into it. It's not only the cooking and the cleaning, but it ties into grocery shopping. Oh, yes, we will cover that one later—I haven't forgotten. At least help her with this while she is pregnant. Wives like it.

🐾 Still going with this one . . .
Don't cook anything that will have a
nauseating smell when cooking.

Nope, I'm not finished with this whole cooking thing yet. This is a hard one for a man to let sink in. Note: She is the one who gets to determine if it's nauseating. Pregnant wives experience nausea, so don't break out the kipper snacks, unless of course that is what she is craving, and don't be surprised if she is. Oh, and that just reminded me—you need to be careful of the mercury levels in fish, especially for your pregnant wife. Kipper snacks might be okay, but I haven't researched it. This was just a random yet important thought. Seriously, your pregnant wife can't have mercury, so be careful with the fish she eats. Research it!

🙂 **Clean the bathrooms (yes, toilets and showers and stuff).**

Your pregnant wife doesn't need to be bent over inhaling those chemicals and fumes. One friend of ours says she can't go five minutes without throwing up and that fumes would make it worse, not to mention the fact that the fumes aren't healthy for the unborn baby. At any rate, chances are you've used the bathroom, so chances are you've helped dirty it. Chances are you should help clean it. While she is pregnant, however, don't just *help* clean it—clean it regularly so she doesn't have to.

I dare say 99% of women have this job to themselves. If they are lucky they fight with the kids and get them to help with it. Forget that business. You be sure it gets done. Take it off your wife's to-do list and put it on yours.

🐞 Give her a phone call now and then just to check on her.

When Kimie and I were expecting our first baby, few people had cell phones. But pagers were all the rage, so I rented one from the hospital. Yes, they actually rented out pagers. I happened to be a telemarketer at the time as I worked through college, so I had access to a phone nonstop. I was anxious all the time, especially during the final six weeks or so of Kimie's pregnancy—so anxious that I called her about eight times a day and asked, "Are you having any contractions, and have you tried to page me? Because if you've tried paging me, this stupid pager is not working."

I seriously made this call around eight times per day, but in the end my wife appreciated it because she knew I was thinking about her. The point is, regularly call (or instant-message or text) your pregnant wife to check on her.

🌼 Pray with your wife every day.

Pray that she and the baby will be healthy, safe, and happy throughout the pregnancy. The first pregnancy is often tenuous. There are a lot of unknowns, and nothing invites calmness like prayer. Include Heavenly Father in this from day one.

MONTH 3

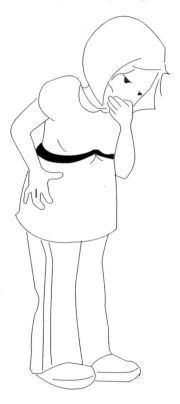

Do your own laundry once in awhile.

You will have a better understanding of why it's so hard to keep track of your socks. That's plenty reason enough, but do it simply so your pregnant wife won't have to.

Skip the last one ... do your own laundry

Not just once in awhile. This will give you fantastic insight to why laundry is so annoying to your wife. Wash it. Fold it. Put it away. Wash it again. Fold it again. Put it away again. Wash it yet again. Fold it yet again. Put it away yet again.

Don't ask her why she always seems so tired.

Are you aware of what a woman's body goes through during pregnancy? Her body is creating a whole other body, a whole other life. Extra blood flow is required, not to mention that the further along the pregnancy gets, the heavier Mom gets, thus causing her to become more tired. And hormone shifts make her tired, too. So now you don't have to ask. You're welcome!

**Don't ever come home from your doctor
appointment and say, "Boy, honey, that sure was
uncomfortable and embarrassing."**

No explanation necessary, I hope. Regardless of what doctor you
visited, it simply won't compare to the doctors your pregnant wife
is dealing with for nine months. No ifs, ands, or buts about it.

Don't ask, "So how much weight have you gained with this pregnancy?"

If she wants to tell you, she will. Or, IF YOU ABSOLUTELY MUST KNOW, go to the doctor with her—they weigh her every time. My wife always told me how much she gained, especially since the doctor instructed her to gain more weight, but I can promise you if that were not the case I would never in a million years have asked. And I wouldn't recommend you asking your wife, either. This one might seem strange, but I'm not shooting from the hip here—I've been through this five times. Weight is definitely a sensitive issue for pregnant women, and understandably so.

If you go to the doctor with your pregnant wife,
don't ask the nurse (at least in front of your wife),
"Is it normal that she gained this much
weight so quickly?"

If you actually make this lame mistake, don't try to cover it up by saying, "My wife has been concerned about this lately." Everyone will know you are really asking it for yourself. And no, fortunately, I have not done this.

Wives don't like this. Period.

When you're walking through the mall, or the park, or anywhere else, don't tell your wife she needs to walk faster.

I muffed this one up all the time, with all five pregnancies. I actually had the audacity to say things like, "Come on, Kimie, we really are in a hurry," or, "Seriously, can you really not walk any faster?" I believe I actually said one time, "Come on, Kimie, that's not a parking spot—let's move it a little faster." Chances are your wife cannot walk fast when she is really pregnant. Repeat that really slowly out loud, so you get it. Repeat after me: "Chances . . . are . . . my . . . wife . . . cannot . . . walk . . . fast . . . when . . . she . . . is . . . really . . . pregnant."

By the way, it doesn't make it any funnier to your wife if you say, "Giddy up, jingle horse, pick up your feet." Not cool.

Anytime Tips

Go to the doctor with your wife as much as possible and share in this whole experience.

Uh, yeah, don't forget this is your baby, too. Show concern for your wife's health and the baby's health. Be sure you are always there for the good news, but especially be sure you are there just in case there is bad news. I strongly believe in going to each doctor appointment with your wife. Also, go with her when she pre-registers at the hospital. Becoming familiar with the layout of the hospital will make things easier on the day the baby is delivered. It will also help your wife to feel more at ease, both in the hospital and during the days leading up to the baby's delivery, especially with your first child.

✤ Do the dishes as often as possible.

No excuses like, "Hey, I work full-time—I shouldn't have to come home and do dishes. She's home all day." So what, do it anyway. Don't worry, you won't become any less masculine. It's too bad we men can't be pregnant for a day—that would be the only way to truly know how it feels. Be thankful that will never happen, and use it to motivate you to do more for your pregnant wife.

✤ Mail your wife a letter telling her how much you love her.

No, email does not count! Letter writing is a dying art. With the advent of email, text messaging, instant messaging, etc., very few people write letters anymore. I'm not going to tell you what to write in the letter; you should be able to come up with this on your own. However, if you really are struggling here, simply tell her how you feel about her, but only if it's good. If nothing more, reminisce about things you have enjoyed together. It shows her you've been thinking of her.

🐾 Don't come home and say, "Holy cow, this house is a mess!"

Even if your intention is only to emphasize that the kids have made a bit of a mess, don't bring it up, unless you've been the one keeping the house clean all this time. And even then, bring it up with the kids, not your wife.

Ultimately, if you complain about the house being a mess, your wife will feel like a failure, and she will feel she is under attack. Think to yourself what you can do to make the house cleaner, without bringing your wife into the equation at all. This is a hot button for your wife, guaranteed. Don't push this button, ever, especially not during pregnancy. Again, your wife will feel that you are blaming her.

🐛 **Don't ask her when she plans to go to the grocery store.**

Okay, here we go. Are you kidding me? Boo-hoo, wah-wah, la–la. Are you all out of Ding Dongs or protein shakes? Oh, big tragedy and super sadness. Hey, while you're at the store, why don't you pick some of that up? This has already been hinted at.

🐛 **Be sure a baby shower is planned for your wife.**

There is nothing unmanly about getting the ball rolling on this. Just see to it that she gets a baby shower. Often, good-intentioned people will discuss putting on a shower, but sometimes it doesn't get done. Again, just get the ball rolling if nothing else. It could be as simple as calling her best friend or a close family member. Just do it. The point is to get started on it so it doesn't fall through the cracks.

MONTH 4

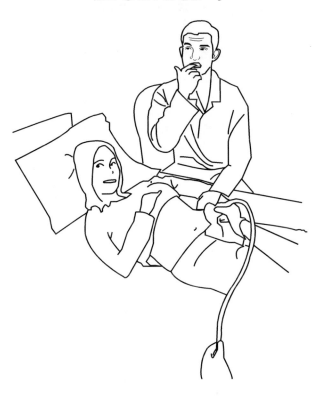

Don't pretend you didn't know
the other kids needed something.

Don't act like you didn't realize one of your other children needed food, a diaper change, help with homework, etc. Don't assume your wife will get to it. She's a saint, so she probably *will* get to it, but you must stop taking advantage of her kindness.

Other examples might be answering the door or the phone. Instead of saying, "Honey, will you get that?" just do it yourself.

Keep her car clean for her, inside and out.

Who cares if it's her car? There are certain things she can't do
very comfortably. And don't allow others to convince you that
by doing this for your wife you are creating some sort of learned
helplessness. I'm just talking about loving her and doing things
for her. It will strengthen your relationship.

Hey, do your wife's laundry!

More laundry stuff. I'm not sorry about it, either. That's right—
you should be doing your laundry anyway, so why not hers, too.
Maybe you could even fold and hang up her clean clothes for
her. Enjoy trying to match all her socks.

Hey, do the kids' laundry!

Wives like it. (Are you noticing somewhat of a laundry theme in this book? Good—go do some laundry.) If your kids are old enough to do laundry (if they can load an MP3 player with music, they can load a washing machine), have them do their own. You could become the official laundry coordinator and wear a badge indicating as much. That way, you don't have to do the laundry, and neither does your pregnant wife. If your kids aren't old enough, or if this is your first kid, this duty is on you.

If she doesn't want you to cook dinner, set and clear the table for her.

But don't look at this as having done something for your wife; don't you all eat at the table? So you're doing this for all of you. Again, this shouldn't be the woman's job—everyone should help. Some women—my own mother, for example—truly don't want people in the kitchen helping them cook. However, I've yet to meet a lady who wouldn't want help clearing and washing the dishes and cleaning the kitchen afterwards. Especially your pregnant wife.

Think back and see if your wife is doing any
jobs you may have been doing but somehow got
out of the habit of, and take them all back.

Are there any jobs you just quit doing, like feeding the dog, taking the garbage can to the curb, pulling weeds, etc.? Take those jobs back.

If she doesn't want to find out the gender of the baby, that should be the final word.

Again, your wife is carrying the baby, so she gets the final say. It's a respect thing, not a power thing. If she wants to find out the baby's gender in advance, let her. Don't say, "I want it to be a surprise." Think about this one—won't you be surprised, regardless of when you find out? At any rate, the wife gets to pick the time. It's just how it should be.

Anytime Tips

🐢 Ask your wife how she's feeling.

Sometimes she just wants to talk and be listened to. (Hint: Look at her when she speaks. Wives like that.) Don't look at the TV, computer, etc. Just look at her.

But don't overdo it—don't just sit and stare. Find a happy medium. Also, morning sickness should be well behind her now, but that doesn't mean she feels spectacular, so just ask her how she is doing.

🐢 Take her to lunch occasionally.

You don't have to go to lunch with your work buddies all the time. Schedule some times to take your wife out during the day. Maybe you can only work that out on days you go to the doctor with your wife, but work it in sometime. This is especially important if your wife is home with small children during the day. She could really use the opportunity to converse with another adult.

Do your chores without being asked.

I always hear men say they would do more housework if they (1) had less yard work, and (2) didn't have to work full-time to support the family. First off, and be honest with yourself, how often does your wife—YOUR PREGNANT WIFE—have to bug you to mow the lawn, take out the garbage, change a light bulb, etc.? We wouldn't even do *our own* chores if our wives didn't see to it that we did. Man up and do your chores, without being reminded or asked. It's ridiculous that I have to even mention this. Don't fool yourself. Your wife works more than full-time between doing the lioness' share of child-rearing and everything else she does. Don't EVER say, "I'm the bread winner—my wife doesn't work." That's pretty thoughtless. Instead say, "My wife works her fanny off at home, taking care of everything, which allows me to go have a career so I can support my family financially." Again, to you I say, MAN UP!

🐾 Turn off the basketball or football game and watch a chick flick with her.

Wives like this. I double-dog dare you to do it during a very important game, such as a playoff game in your favorite sport. I understand this is NOT an easy one. In fact, this could be the hardest one in the book. And by the way, if you're not a sports fan you're still not off the hook. It applies to any vice you have. Put aside your vice and watch a chick flick with your wife. Shut off the stupid computer, the lame video-gaming system, your electric guitar—whatever it is. Stop for a while and hang with her.

🐞 Show excitement about the fact the baby is going to be born.

If you sound upset, depressed, or perturbed during your wife's pregnancy, she may have a hard time dealing with it, when normally she would be just fine. And whether this baby was planned or not, always be very positive in both words and actions.

Don't ever complain about the fact that you two are having a baby. Even if you weren't planning on having kids (or more kids), the man is not the one who is going to nearly double in size—that's how the woman feels—and have to recover from pregnancy and childbirth. No complaining!

Don't say, "If you weren't pregnant we could go . . ." or, "If you weren't pregnant we could do . . ." Oh, and here's another one: Don't blame her for being pregnant, if it wasn't "good timing." Remember, both of you were involved in the baby's creation.

The coolest thing you will ever do is be a father. Show excitement and appreciation for that at all times.

🖋 Offer to do any job that was hers.

Don't look at marriage as 50/50, where each person gives 50% of the effort. If you look at it as 60/40, each spouse— always doing 60%—can make up for what the other cannot currently do. But while your wife is pregnant, it is not *ever* to be 60/40 in your favor, but always in her favor. And don't complain about it.

When you get home, do the dishes. Wives like it. I know, I've already mentioned this, but it is big. They deal with dishes every single day, multiple times. Take that burden away while she's pregnant.

Speaking of bath towels (yes, I know I wasn't talking about bath towels at all), have you ever noticed how often your wife is washing and folding bath towels? Wash them and fold them for her, or at least get one of your children to fold them. That is our ten-year-old's job. It's not always neat, but my pregnant wife doesn't have to do it. Sometimes coordinating this list is all that's required. You're not really expected to do it all yourself like she usually does.

While you're at it, dust the house.

MONTH 5

Turn the TV off—sometimes she just needs it quiet.

Don't be afraid of the silence, Captain Remote. If TV is not your vice, figure out what is and ignore that in exchange for time with your wife. Just be sure it's quiet time.

Don't make fun of her pregnancy clothes.

Especially don't make fun of the pants with the white, stretchy front panel. Remember, her clothes are all about comfort and function, not style. News flash—she is not that fond of wearing them. Most women don't look forward to gaining forty pounds or more and purchasing the clothes to accommodate it. Simply put, they don't need your commentary regarding their clothes.

On this note, something else not to say is, "Didn't you wear that yesterday?" Don't blow it with this one, man.

Carry the groceries into the house for your wife, especially if you failed to go and buy them for her.

Note here that I did not say, *"Help* her carry the groceries." I said do it *for* her. After you've hauled them in the house, decide which of the goods you are going to use to make dinner. Oh, and by the way, don't leave her alone to put the groceries away. That job sucks, so help her out.

It sounds silly, but let her wear your pajamas.

My wife was frustrated one night when she couldn't fit into any of her pajamas. I wish I had seen this coming, especially since it's our fifth child (duh), but we hadn't purchased her any pregnancy-size pajamas, or maybe she gave them away. At any rate, offer your wife your pajamas. My wife loves wearing my big, baggy flannels. In fact, my most comfortable pair of pajama pants were kept from me for nearly four months. I actually have them on as I type this one. Big pajama pants are cool, so let your wife borrow yours, or BUY HER SOME HUGE PAJAMA PANTS OF HER OWN.

By the way, real men wear pajama pants!

No giving her guilt trips if she doesn't quite feel up to going camping, or on a long road trip, or whatever.

Think about this one. There is nothing quite like stuffing several months of pregnancy into a tight little mummy bag. While you're at it, wake up and make her some greasy bacon-and-sausage breakfast burritos. Such a good idea.

Don't say (and I did the other day), "Do you realize how hard it is having five kids?" Of course she does.

Hey, this whole pregnancy and childbirth thing messes with our (men's) heads, too. I just wish it wouldn't have been my outside voice that I used. In other words, I wish I would have only thought it. I swears, I is so stupids. Where's that filter? Actually, this one may only apply to me unless you already have multiple children, but it's just another example of the dumb things we men have the potential of saying and doing.

Anytime Tips

* Wubb 'er nooble (that means massage her head).

This, when done correctly, is about the most relaxing thing in the world. She deserves to be relaxed.

Start at the base of her skull, on the back of her head. Press in with your thumbs. Fingers are high on her shoulders for support, and then slowly but firmly press upward. When you reach as high as your thumbs will go, press in and hold for five seconds. Do this fifteen to twenty times.

Then massage her temples, slowly and firmly, in a counterclockwise, circular motion. Use your index, middle, and fourth fingers for this. Do this for forty-five seconds, then move up a little higher on her temples and massage there, in the same manner, for forty-five seconds. Then move up one last time, just a little, and repeat for an additional forty-five seconds.

Next, open both hands wide and massage her entire head. Do this for at least one minute, and then finish up with slow, circular motions on the eyebrows.

I'm not a massage therapist, but I do know what feels good. I also know that it helps my wife a lot, and that anyone in his or her right mind would love it.

Change your other kids' diapers.

Do this so your wife doesn't have to get nauseated by it. Don't make her do the bend and sniff! Seriously, it doesn't matter what you are doing, you can always take a break from it and change a diaper. Why wouldn't you? Who was the one who decided it was the mom's job to always change the diaper?

Admit it—you usually pretend you don't know the diaper needs to be changed. If you wait long enough, your wife will have to take care of it, right? No more! From now on you can't even get away with saying, "I checked a few minutes ago and he wasn't poopy."

It's time to step it up, men.

Don't tell her she's looking more pregnant lately.

Hopefully this one requires no explanation. Okay, maybe it does, because I have heard this one before, sadly enough. Even if it's completely innocent, why would anyone make this statement? Perhaps you are a man experiencing hair loss—I am, to some extent—so one of the last things you need to hear is, "You're looking balder lately." This is the ultimate common-sense thing not to do. It is even worse than saying, "Wow, Grandma, you sure are looking older lately."

Even if you somehow mean it in a complimentary way, don't say it. Take, for example, the following experience I had with my wife, Kimie. I was whining to her one day that my hair was receding and turning gray—well, more of a silver/white/platinum, I suppose. At any rate, she said I need not worry about my follicle situation, that the changes actually made me look more "distinguished." You see, while she meant well, I took that comment to mean that I can now more easily be "distinguished" from the good-looking guys.

🐞 **Make sure your wife takes time for herself.**

Your wife will feel guilty if she ever does anything for herself, rather than always putting this baby first. Make sure she has time for herself—and that she takes it! For example, if you find yourself sitting down and relaxing, be sure your wife is doing the same thing. If she is not, figure out what you can do for her so she can.

🐞 **Hug her, kiss her, hold her hand in public even more.**

She doesn't feel very attractive right now. Let her know she is. Enough said.

No, not enough said! If you take the time to really admire your wife right now, while she is pregnant, you will discover something. There is a different glow or aura about your wife while she is pregnant. Someone pointed this out to me long ago, and now I see it in my wife, relatives, or close friends. It's there even before the physical signs of pregnancy. A pregnant woman glows, and you will find it adds to her attractiveness. If you don't see it, figure out why and find it. If you never find it, okay, but don't EVER let your wife feel that you are not attracted to her.

🦠 Don't let her (or you) forget that she still has dreams and aspirations.

Your wife is probably excited to be having this baby, especially if this is her first. However, the novelty does wear off at some point. Sometimes an expectant woman starts to feel she is nothing more than a mother. Your wife is much more than a wife, and much more than a mother, just like you are much more than what you do for a career. The point is to help her maintain balance.

Motherhood is ordained of God. I can't stress this enough. My wife feels the greatest thing she can accomplish is being the best mother she can be. It's the most important aspect of her life, but she also has aspirations and dreams and goals aside from that. Help your wife reach her full potential in all facets of her life. She has talents and meaningful contributions that this world needs. She will discover new strengths and meanings during her pregnancy, and she may even replace old dreams with new ones. Let her decide this, and then support her all the way. Encourage her all the way. Honor her.

Take a Break . . . for YOU.

Okay, are you overwhelmed? Don't be. Remember, nobody is really saying to do EVERYTHING. Just be aware of all your wife is doing, needing, and going through. This book is about her and her needs; however, you need to lookout for yourself, too.

Take some time and be sure you're enjoying your job, or school, or whatever phase of life you're in. Be sure you're taking breaks, getting enough sleep, eating right, and exercising. Be sure you have some kind of hobby you enjoy. If you don't have a hobby, get one. It can't be all work all the time. And hobbies don't have to be expensive, if that is a concern. When was the last time you simply hung out with one of your buddies? Call him and go to lunch or do something. The point is you need to take care of yourself before you can properly take care of others. Your happiness is as important in all of this as your wife's is.

This book was not intended to be memorized, just implemented a bit at a time. Keep it around and refer to it on occasion. It's the helpful guide I wish I would've had starting back in 1995. Take it for what it is. And I can't stress this enough: As important as it is to do as much of this for your wife as you can, do not leave yourself out. You have to look out for yourself. Before you move on to the last sixty suggestions, pat yourself on the back for all you've been willing to do so far. Just reading this book and showing your willingness to improve speaks volumes about you. Outside of reading this book, just knowing you're trying to improve your relationship is plenty of reason to congratulate yourself. Being a real man is a tough job. Keep it up. Just remember to keep track of yourself in all of this. Reward yourself sometimes.

MONTH 6

Run errands for her.

Have you ever noticed how well your pregnant wife fits behind a steering wheel? Take notice of it when she starts to really progress in the pregnancy. Pay particular attention to how awkward it is for her to slide in behind the steering wheel, and how far away from it she has to sit. Moms/wives have to do this little ritual quite a bit, and driving will get even less enjoyable for them with each kid they have because they first have to load all the kids in the car. The point, if it's not already obvious, is that you should run as many little errands for her as possible, because at some point they will not seem little to her. Eliminate the steering-wheel ritual for your pregnant wife as much as possible.

Don't ask her how much weight she has gained.

Yes, I've touched on this. I know I don't have to explain this one. Pregnant women gain weight. Be done with it.

Give your wife an opportunity every day to take a nap.

Especially on the weekend when you're home a lot. Or at the very least, make sure she has time to put her feet up and "veg." On Saturday mornings, I lock the bedroom door so my wife can sleep in while I get up with the kids. It doesn't count if you lock the kids out while you remain in the bedroom. Get up and take care of them while your wife rests. Don't forget about your other kids throughout all of this. That's a whole other book, though.

Don't say, "Do you feel as miserable as you look?"

This is self-explanatory, but if you actually try it once, you can come up with your own reasons not to say it. If you actually say it, you have to get in touch with me and let me know how it ends.

Do say, "Wow, honey, you are glowing today!"

Be sure to sound sincere rather than scripted or like you're trying to earn something by making the comment. This needs to turn into your saying something positive to her every day. Pregnancy is a beautiful thing. I already said it, but the glow of motherhood is real, and you will notice it the moment you find out your wife is pregnant. Women literally glow when they are pregnant. Take notice of it, respect and love it, and let her know she is glowing.

Don't say, "For being pregnant, you sure look good."

Let's see, what else can we come up with? Ooh, I know, "You're a good athlete for a girl," or, "You're strong for a lady." Get the point? Remember, pregnant women glow.

When you're at an appointment with your wife, don't ask the doctor if there is any way he or she can be sure the baby will be born either before or after March Madness.

Put in any event or date you want, but this happens all too often—Dad thinks he has something so important that the baby must be born around his schedule. It's not just dads who feel this way; there are plenty of extended family members who will want to give your wife a limited number of acceptable dates for the baby to be delivered. Think back to when you and your fiancé were trying to pick a wedding date. There were a lot of people telling you what would be best and appreciated, right? Multiply that by ten when having a baby—people actually suggest dates.

Oh, and don't let another question be, "So is increased flatulence normal with pregnancy?" It's not funny. Wives don't like it!

Don't ask, "So have you noticed if you're getting any stretch marks?"

Furthermore, don't follow it up with "If you do have stretch marks, are they always going to be there, or will they go away?" Be smart, sensitive, and use common sense. And by the way, if she does have stretch marks, don't point them out. I'm pretty sure she knows where they are.

Another point on stretch marks: Don't even bring them up in a corny way that may seem complimentary, such as, "At least they make a cool design—you know, kind of like a roadmap."

Anytime Tips

 Change the bed sheets weekly.

Chores like this become even more tedious for your wife when she's pregnant. Plus, everyone likes climbing into clean, crisp sheets, so why wouldn't she? Let her experience this weekly. That may mean you have to do some laundry. "You're kidding! Laundry? I'll turn into a woman!" Hey, knock it off.

 Massage your wife's feet whenever she asks.

Because she likes it, that's why, and that's plenty reason enough.

☙ `Bag that last one. Rub her feet `*`before`*
   `she asks.`

Why should she have to ask? Why do I have to put this one in here?

☙ `Make the bed.`

Don't say, "She was in it when I left for work." Instead, tell her to leave it until you get home from work.

Think about this, you slept in it too. It doesn't matter who got out of it last. Pamper your pregnant wife. There is no such thing as doing too much for her. Don't allow yourself to not to do for her because you're afraid that if you give her an inch she will take a yard. In fact, just give her the yard to begin with!

🐝 Accept her mood swings.

I've already talked about her being a little extra-sensitive, but this is worth repeating. She will have mood swings because her hormones are all over the place. PLUS SHE IS PREGNANT—SHE FEELS LOUSY. She is justified in having some mood swings. And maybe there won't be any, but be ready for them, and be willing and able to overlook them. Keep in mind that nothing she says is personal, unless of course you ignore the advice within these pages.

🐝 Wash the fingerprints and marks off the walls and windows.

I just noticed fingerprints on the walls in my house and thought to myself, "Why didn't Kimie notice those and clean them up? Holy cow, they're on the piano, too. Why can't she see them and clean them?" Wait a minute. I just had a novel idea—what if I were to clean them up? If I do, I better not tell her I did it, because that kind of shot to the old ticker could send her into early labor. Maybe I'll just do it because I love her. Not to mention they are my walls and my piano, too. It only makes sense that I would help take care of the stuff I've always insisted should be the duty of the woman. I guess I could always yell, 'Hey, pregnant woman, quit moping around and do something productive! I go to work all day.'" Blah, blah, blah, blah.

After the kids are in bed, offer to go grocery shopping for your wife.

Here we go again! Take her list, and bring back any treat(s) she wants. She's pregnant—she deserves it. Wait until the kids are in bed, so she doesn't have to look after them while you're gone. And by the way, your wife doesn't have to share. And think about it, you're not just doing it for your wife when it comes right down to it, you're doing it for yourself and your kids (where applicable). I will assume your wife isn't the only one eating the groceries she goes shopping for.

On a regular basis, offer to run her bathwater.

Put bubbles in it, and something for her to rest her head on. Have candles for the lighting—that way she can relax more. While she's pregnant she won't be able to relax in Jacuzzis or hot tubs, so give her a nice warm bath regularly. Especially as the pregnancy progresses and her back starts to hurt.

Heat her bath towels.

A few minutes before your wife gets out of the tub, put her bath towel in the clothes dryer and warm it up for her, then run it to her as quickly as possible (Hint: fold it up right when you pull it from the dryer—it will stay warmer longer.)

If you haven't run a bath for her and discover she is in the shower, do the towel thing for sure.

Be sure to have two towels. Women like to wrap one of them around their head.

If you can't put her towels in the dryer, buy her a towel rack that doubles as a towel warmer. Just figure something out here.

At least once a week, massage lotion into your wife's hands.

Wives like it. This is a simple task that helps her relax, as any massage would, but it also shows her the affection she longs for. (Note: After the baby is born, your wife will be washing her hands a lot, especially if you're not helping much with the diapers. Rub lotion into her hands for sure at this point. Her hands will need moisturizing.) It is especially nice to use your thumbs to massage the palms of her hands in kind of a forward kneading motion. Again, I'm not a massage therapist, but I know what feels really swell.

Don't try to pretend that the sympathy weight you're gaining will somehow help her feel better about her situation.

"Hey, sweet thing, can you believe how much weight I've gained since you got pregnant?" Say that one really slowly and aloud so you can experience firsthand how brilliant it sounds. It's like asking a completely bald man if your hairline is receding—when you have a full head of hair. The point? Don't draw any additional attention to the fact that your pregnant wife is gaining weight. More about *your* weight gain later.

As nice as it may sound, don't say, "You know, you don't even really look pregnant, at least until you stand sideways."

It's a good thing to be nice and try to say the right things, but sometimes trying too hard can be much worse than saying nothing at all! Always be sure to turn the filter to FULL POWER.

Anytime Tips

🕮 Take her on a date for some alone time with you.

Generally, a man enjoys going out with his wife. A lot of my friends do this once per week. If you're not taking her out each week, at least do so twice a month. Don't forget your relationship during her pregnancy. This is something that tends to take a back seat as you have kids. Take the time now to make it a priority.

🕮 Learn to say you're sorry.

Don't over-think this—just be the first one to apologize. It honestly doesn't matter who is right. And it if does turn out you were right, and if it is actually important that it be made known that you were right, it does not give you license to be mean, sarcastic, arrogant—or any other not-so-charming adjective—about it.

Remember when I told you to write your wife a letter? If you can't find anything to write to her about, perhaps an apology is in order, in the form of a letter.

This is always important, whether your wife is pregnant or not, but I will remind you that her emotions, while she is pregnant, are a little extra-sensitive. Say you're sorry, mean it, and then move on.

Sit in whatever room she wants to.

In other words, just be where she is to show that you enjoy her company. The TV doesn't need to be on—just sit in a quiet room with her and don't worry about being entertained.

Often, couples are split up in the evening so each can do something different. Spend more time just being together.

🐾 Don't be mad at her because she bought this book.

This could be the only desperate plea for help she gives you. I've hit these brick walls for all of us—no need for you to. Now keep on . . . keep on loving and doing for your wife. Honestly, she just wants you to be part of her pregnancy. If you quit reading at this point, at least go make some dinner and do some laundry. Maybe even just go hold her hand.

🐾 Take the kids out for an hour and give your wife some alone time.

This also gives you and your other kids some solid bonding time. Don't forget the kids are yours, too. Don't ever look at it as babysitting your kids. You don't babysit your own kids—you spend time with them. You raise them! You love them! You babysit other people's kids. Got it? In fact, an hour is not enough, so make it at least two hours.

MONTH 8

Get the kids ready for school.

You may have to wake up thirty minutes earlier. Your wife really does need more sleep—pregnancy takes a lot out of her. Keep in mind that she is not going to get much sleep during the newborn months, either, so get in the habit now of getting the other kids ready.

Buy her flowers.

There are a lot of things your pregnant wife doesn't like so much anymore, but flowers are *not* among them. GET HER SOME! You can find nice, inexpensive floral arrangements at places other than floral shops. Flowers don't represent money spent on your wife—they represent the time you spent thinking about her.

Fluff her pillows before she gets in bed.

Women like this. If she goes to bed before you, just run to the bedroom first and do this for her. This is a really simple one, but it is more meaningful than it appears. Why? It shows her you have been thinking of her. We hit on this a lot in this book. She needs to know you think about her.

Tuck her in bed at night.

Or at least offer to. Some may feel this is babying her too much. Maybe she won't like having you tuck her in, but my wife sure does. It's a secure feeling for her. It's an "I love you" reminder, an "I'm thinking of you." It's just another simple way to pamper your pregnant wife.

If it's winter, warm up your wife's side of the bed.

You can buy a $15 space heater, an electric blanket, a heated mattress pad, or whatever—just warm it up for her. If nothing more, lie down on her side of the bed for at least five minutes before she gets in. She deserves instant comfort. If it's summer, turn her pillow to the cool side for her every seventeen to twenty minutes. Just kidding. But if it's summer, know this: A woman who is pregnant is not comfortable at all. The heat is the worst. Help take that temperature down a notch. There are pillows out there now that stay much cooler—I believe they are loaded with comfy little beads. I dare say it's worth considering.

Don't say, especially during the summer, "Wow, I'm hot. Are you hot?"

Y-E-S! She IS hot! She's roasting! She's carrying around thirty-plus pounds of a personal space heater, so, again, YES, she is hot. Yes, she wants a shaved ice or a snow cone. No, she doesn't want to have to go get it herself. It should all be coming together for you now, brother. It's all about doing nice things for her, while avoiding making ridiculous comments.

Buy her a body pillow to sleep with.

Your expecting wife deserves all the extra comfort she can get, so buy her one of those body-length pillows. She can cuddle with it and put it between her knees, or under her tummy, or whatever she wants, to help her get comfortable at night. This ties in with letting her wear your pajamas—everything needs to be bigger for her while she is pregnant. (I guess that doesn't sound so nice, but it's true.) You can purchase body pillows at most stores that sell everything under the sun. Just come home with one someday, and your wife will be your new best friend.

Figure out a way for her to go to bed early.

When a lady is pregnant, she looks forward to getting into bed each night. The problem is that there is usually too much going on for this to happen at a decent hour, especially if there are other kids in the house. It could be a number of things, so your job is to figure out what is keeping your wife from going to bed early now and then, and make it so she can.

Do the ironing.

For one thing, she may not be able to reach the ironing board, and I hope this doesn't sound rude. The whole ergonomics of the ironing situation does not foster comfort and success for a pregnant woman. However, I must admit I did not even come close to doing this for my wife. I have always made things worse by ironing them. I can iron wrinkles into the ironing-board cover. I've been asked where I buy my pleated shirts. Enough said. Just know I wish I would have done this for my wife while she was pregnant, and you should do it for yours. It is an inconvenient task for her.

Bathe the kids.

If you have other kids in the house, take over this duty, because I'm sure it has been your wife's responsibility. Just for fun, stuff a butternut squash under your shirt as you bend over the bathtub to bathe the kids. Note how wonderful it feels as the edge of the tub smashes it into your abdomen. Too bad the squash can't kick your insides at the same time.

Anytime Tips

 Allow her first and last say in the naming of the baby.

By now the two of you (or the thirty-plus of you, since family always insists on getting involved) have discussed, ad nauseam, what to name your baby. I know a lot of guys who feel it is their patriarchal duty to be the one who names the baby. Whatever—the woman is the one who carries the baby, so she clearly deserves more say than the man does. It's a rite of passage . . . *she* is giving birth! Do be aware, though, that she may be influenced by painkillers, especially in the case of a C-section. For example, my wife delivered our last baby via C-section and was therefore admonished to be on painkillers while still in the hospital. They made her feel very good—so good, in fact, that she said, "I want you to name this baby because I love you." I literally could have named our new daughter Biff, and my wife would have been fine with it. So, be sure the naming of the baby is not under the influence of narcotics.

Ideally you will both agree, but if not, allow the name to be your wife's idea. *She carried and delivered.*

🐾 **Help the kids with their homework while your wife puts her feet up.**

In our house, my wife usually helps the kids with their homework before I return home from work. However, the kids need to be able to come to either parent for this. Do whatever it takes to be sure your wife doesn't have to do this all the time. Truthfully, a lot of times this is exactly why Kimie didn't get to bed early, or even on time.

🦟 Every day, be aware of her feelings and how she is doing.

Don't expect a seemingly good day to be peachy for your pregnant wife. She has a lot going on. Just be aware—now more than ever—of her and her needs.

🦟 Overall, be extra-sensitive and understanding with her.

As mentioned, a woman's hormones fluctuate a lot while she is pregnant, which means she can experience mood swings and other unpleasant symptoms. This is the best time to make all those changes in your character that you've been wanting or needing to make. For example, if you have a short fuse, now is the best time to fix that. If you are sarcastic in a rude way, now is the best time to change that.

And if you are a man of little or no patience, you absolutely must fix that now.

🦁 **Rub her shoulders, neck, and lower back EVERY night.**

She flat out deserves this. Think about it—you have either been to a massage therapist, or at the very least have had a wonderful shoulder rub. Tension just melts away as you are being massaged. We tend to store tension high in our back—near our neck and between our shoulder blades. I know Kimie does. Give your wife a good rubbing there. Also rub her lower back. Wives like it, and while they are pregnant they really need it. Maybe wubb 'er nooble every other day and then massage her back the other days. Just a thought.

MONTH 9

Don't say, "You look like you're going to explode. Do you feel like you are?"

Yes, she feels like she is—and often wishes she would. Good job on pointing it out! I've done this. I've always possessed the uncanny ability to eloquently state the obvious. So let me state the obvious here: DON'T SAY IT! Wives don't like it.

While driving in the car, take it easy around corners and over bumps and stuff.

Remember, your pregnant wife really is uncomfortable. To know what that feels like, overdo it next time at Thanksgiving, then go swing on a tire swing (you have to spin it), or go jump on a trampoline or jog . . . or better yet, run a bunch of wind sprints.

This is especially important during the first and third trimesters, when she will be extra-nauseated and/or uncomfortable.

Get up half an hour earlier and make breakfast for the kids.

Oh, and for your wife, too. She needs more rest than you do. And while you're at it, make your own lunch to take to work.

Don't complain to her about your hard day at work.

Whatever problems you had at work, just leave them there. This is stress your wife doesn't need to deal with, not to mention the fact that she could be having a tough day dealing with all she has to deal with. If you must vent, be careful how you do it. Avoid being too negative.

Don't try to convince a pregnant lady how fat or out of shape you feel.

This goes back to your sympathy weight from month seven. Chances are you do feel, even look, out of shape. This could especially be the case if you have gained any sympathy (lazy) pounds. Each of my buddies and I gained weight once we were married. I gained even more weight once my wife got pregnant with our first child. I promise you there was no sympathy for my poundage and me. Don't even mention it. If you feel you must, still don't. Instead, cry yourself a river, build a bridge, and then get over it. Or, as a friend suggests, do something about it.

Similarly, don't complain to your wife about how bad your feet hurt or how much your back aches. All pregnant ladies' feet and backs hurt at some point, especially during the last trimester. So don't come home from work and announce that your feet and back are killing you, or any other part of your body, for that matter.

Don't say, "Man, I wish I could just get comfortable."

This ties nicely into the last one, for obvious reasons, but I feel the unfortunate need to explain, because I'm a man who has messed up on almost everything is this book at least once.

Anyway, this is especially important when you're in bed at night. Try stuffing a few loaves of bread or a partially inflated soccer ball beneath your shirt and then sleeping. I had two ruptured discs in my back for seven years and could not sleep at night, yet anytime my wife was pregnant I felt guilty complaining about it. My discomfort was no sacrifice, but hers was.

And don't ever say, "I wish I could get some sleep." Just don't.

Don't ever make the elephant-march sound when your pregnant wife walks into the room.

Yes, I did do this. Not funny, apparently. To make it worse, there were other people in the room. I don't remember that aspect of the event, but my wife, as I write this one, insists that was the case. This is bringing up bad memories.

Having not learned from this pathetic experience, I tried it out on a pregnant coworker. Turns out she didn't find it any more hilarious than my wife did. On that same day at work, however, a male coworker blew it even worse than I did. He was talking about a big, fat Rottweiler he came across, and he said, in front of this pregnant coworker, "That dog was as big as Jessica" (name changed for anonymity).

What's my point? We guys say dumb things, and it's not cool. So guys, again, turn your filter on high before you speak. It's just good practice in any situation.

As your wife is being examined toward the end of her pregnancy, don't say, "Just don't be mad if you're not dilated yet."

Holy cow, there is nothing your wife will want to hear more than "You have really dilated." When they don't hear this, they are very disappointed and sometimes a bit depressed. For their sake, let it go. It's a very rare occasion when they are happy to *not* be dilated.

What? You don't know what dilated means? Not cool—I thought you had been going to doctor appointments with her.

While your wife is in labor at the hospital, don't talk about the food she has been served but can't eat.

I learned this the hard way when my wife had our first child. It was a fairly long labor, nearly twenty hours, which isn't as long as some, but long nonetheless. During this time my wife, Kimie, was not allowed to eat anything. Three meals were brought to her throughout the day, even though, again, she could not eat. Her mother and I ate those meals—yes, in front of her. Kimie was seemingly okay with this until the last meal came accompanied by a large (Frisbee-sized) chocolate-chip cookie. My mother-in-law and I were so considerate and kept telling each other to eat the cookie. "You have it." "No, that's okay, you eat the cookie," and on and on. This went on for a couple minutes until my wife could no longer tolerate it. No need to repeat what she said, but suffice it to say she was eager for both her mother and me to become silent.

Don't say, "If I were you I would just deliver the baby naturally—no epidural."

Somebody very close to me actually told me, "I don't believe in epidurals. She should just be in there delivering naturally." He didn't think she should have Pitocin to induce labor either—he thought she should be stomping around the hospital to encourage labor. I couldn't believe it. He clearly didn't understand what his wife was about to go through.

Hey, if your wife decides to do this all on her own, naturally, that's swell. However, it is not your place to push this. If you feel it is, perhaps you should consider having a root canal, Novocain free. You know, all natural, like it should be done— like a real man would do it.

Probably the best thing to say to your wife is, "How have you decided to deliver this baby?"

Anytime Tips

After the baby is born, while you're still at the hospital, feed your wife (especially after a C-section).

Yes, feed her as you would a child. Her core/abdominal muscles will be a mess, so don't allow her to lean forward to feed herself. Just take care of her. No, this is not babying her—this is loving her. And don't assume she is not being tough enough if she can't do this, or many other things, on her own. C-sections are tough to come back from. Pregnancy in general is hard for a woman to come back from.

Be aware that after a C-section your wife will be very reliant upon you for at least three to four weeks. HAVE

PATIENCE. Be willing to do whatever, whenever, wherever because you love her and want her to heal. Time will pass, and after awhile things will be back to normal. As it passes, make sure it does so gently for your wife.

🐾 Stay with your wife in the hospital.

Especially after a C-section. It may not always be possible (especially if you have other children, though hopefully you have family who can help), but as much as possible, be at the hospital with your wife and new baby. Again, be involved with the whole process.

Part of why you need to be with your wife is explained a little later. If nothing else be there to help her up, to rub her feet, to hold her hand—to do whatever she needs, period. You may be there to simply play the role of gatekeeper, to keep things calm and quiet for your wife.

Your wife needs to heal, so ask the nurse to take the baby back to the nursery.

If the nurse says, "Your baby is crying a lot in the nursery so we need to bring him to your room," remind them that your wife is healing and that the baby can come in after your wife has had more time to sleep. Feed your baby, and then send him or her back—for your wife's sake. Perhaps you can go back to the nursery too for some of that bonding, but make sure your wife can rest. We actually had one nurse who kept bringing our third child back to my wife. The nurse said each time, "Your baby just keeps crying in the nursery." One time, I awoke in the middle of the night to find my wife crying. She could not get any sleep because the nurse refused to take the baby to the nursery. I got up, held the baby for a moment, and then wheeled him back to the nursery, where at 2:00 in the morning there were four or five nurses sitting in a circle playing cards. There wasn't one baby in the nursery—that would have stifled their card game. I spoke my peace, left our son there, and returned to my wife's room to play gatekeeper.

🐾 While in the hospital, remember that your wife is healing and may not feel like being social.

It's not always the case, but with a C-section, especially after the epidural wears off, she will not feel like visiting, so take strict control of who visits, when they visit, and for how long. Always keep your wife's best interests forefront in your mind. This is also very important when you get home from the hospital, for at least a couple weeks. Others may be offended, but your wife will be defended. I just made that up—it's cool, huh?

Many people with loving intentions want to hold your baby and have photo opportunities, and they want to hold him or her longer than anyone else, and on and on and on. Wife and baby need rest, and there will be plenty of time for baby to be seen. Baby doesn't have to be passed around like a hot potato, and Mom shouldn't have to worry about this happening. It's your job to prevent all of this. Take over! Be nice, but again, if people get offended, they get offended. Your concern is your wife and baby.

While in the hospital with your wife and baby, remember that the TV can be annoying, especially if you're the one in charge of the remote.

It's her remote, so leave her and the TV alone! You're probably watching TV because you're bored. Hopefully your wife is sleeping at this point. This is a good time to

start bonding with your baby. Yes, you read it correctly—
your baby. Go bond. Leave the TV behind. You can do it.
And truthfully, your baby won't bond with you as much
during these hours in the hospital, but you will bond with
him or her. Things will start to get a little more frustrating
once you get home, so take advantage of this opportunity.

Conclusion

First off, is this book all-inclusive? As I said in the introduction, probably not, but aren't you glad I kept it to the number of items I did? I'm sure we could keep adding to it, and I just may. (Okay, I will right now: Don't ever say, "My wife is having a baby," or, "My wife is expecting." Why would you say that? You're both having the baby—you're both expecting.) But you need to walk before you can run, so start taking some baby steps, albeit large baby steps.

Now that you are finished you may be thinking that some of this book is ridiculous, and that's great as long as you are at least *thinking* now. But really it's not so ridiculous. When did it become ridiculous to cater to your wife, especially when she is giving up so much? You need to love your wife like you never thought you could love anyone. Love her even as Jesus loves her. Women sacrifice a lot, sometimes everything, to bring a child into this world. Sometimes the child does not survive. Sometimes the mother doesn't make it. With everything that could potentially go wrong during pregnancy and delivery, you need to make it as beautiful an experience as possible for your wife. Then, get on your knees and thank God for giving you a mother who was willing to do the same for you.

Do not underestimate the toll pregnancy and childbirth takes on your wife. Appreciate her and respect her. Motherhood is a calling from God, so be sure you treat your wife like He expects you to treat her (Ephesians 5:25 sets the expectations pretty clearly). Think back to how you felt about her the first time you held her hand. Think back to the day you got married, and how you felt about her that day. Take both of those incredible days, combine those feelings, and share that increased love with your wife throughout the pregnancy.

A long time ago my wife said, "Once you have a baby, it's never about you anymore—it's all about the baby." She did not say this because she was bitter, but because she felt her priorities had to change at that moment, and perhaps forever. All the more reason to, especially while your wife is pregnant, make it all about her.

I've been thinking a lot about all of this. Kimie's and my fifth child was a scheduled C-section, and the birth went very well. As I thought about why, I remembered the blessings my wife received, and the many prayers in her and the baby's behalf, and that triggered these few final suggestions.

- Include the Lord in your family planning and in preparing for the arrival of a baby.

- Pray in faith that the medical staff will be guided and inspired by the Lord.

- Pray together often for all to be well, yet be willing to accept God's will.

I am a regular guy, so if I can pick up on this, anyone can. And should. This is experience, common sense, and gut feeling, not science, and that's why anyone can do it. Anyone can use common sense. I hope you see that this book is really just about giving yourself to, and for, your wife. Sometimes *not* doing things for your wife is as damaging as purposely mistreating her. Be aware of her feelings. And when she is no longer pregnant, be willing to keep on doing things for her and loving her. Wives like it! She deserves it, and you don't want to ever regret having not done it. I'm sure you agree. It's common sense.

Your Section

Gentlemen, please use this page and the next to take notes and jot down reminders for yourself of other things your wife needs. Everyone's needs vary, and you should know her pretty well by now, so make your own list and refer to it often.

1.

2.

3.

4.

5.

6.

7.

8.

9.

10.

About the Author

Michael J. Snapp is passionate about five things: family, faith, fitness, friends, and of course, common sense. He has worked in higher education for more than a decade as a career counselor, instructor, and administrator. He holds a bachelor's degree in communications and a master's degree in educational counseling. Through his education and his professional and life experiences, Michael has learned that everything is better with a little common sense. He is incredibly happily married, has five amazing children, and lives in Utah.